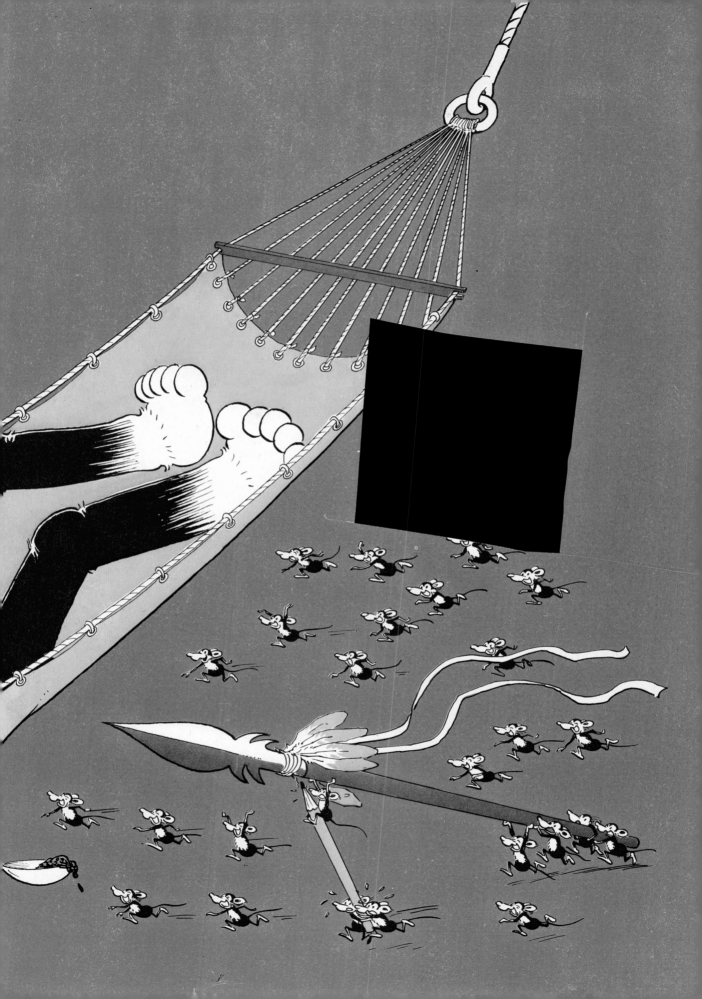

Printed and Published in Great Britain by D. C. THOMSON & CO., LTD.,185 Fleet Street, London EC4A 2HS.
© D. C. THOMSON & CO., LTD., 1981.
ISBN 0 85116 200 2

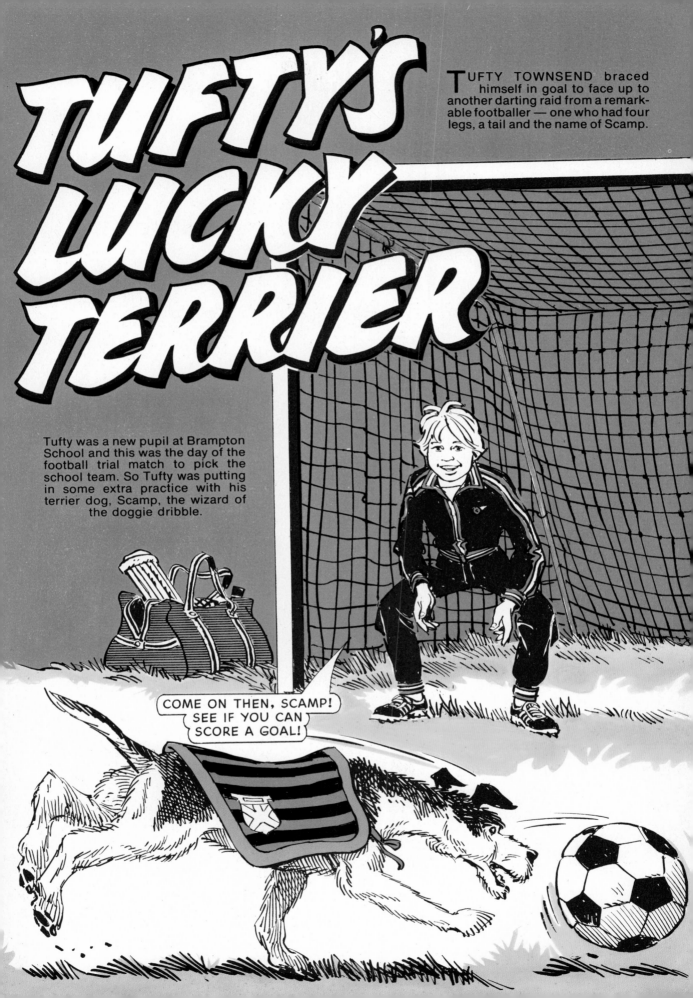

Leaving Scamp at home, Tufty dashed to the school playing fields where the Games Master selected the sides.

RIGHT! YOU PLAY IN THE STRIPED JERSEY TEAM, TOWNSEND.

Midway through the first half, Tufty missed a sitter.

OH, NO!

WHAT A MISS!

Then in the second half, he stumbled over the ball and bang went another scoring chance.

DRAT! I'VE TRIPPED MYSELF!

Next day, the chosen team was pinned up on the board. And Tufty's name wasn't listed!

HARD LUCK, TUFTY! YOU HAVEN'T BEEN PICKED!

Tufty was downcast as he ambled home at lunchtime. But he perked up when Scamp bounded to meet him. And the happy terrier gave Tufty a brainwave.

WE'LL GO AND WATCH THE GAME, SCAMP, AND YOU CAN BE OUR LUCKY MASCOT. I'LL DRESS YOU UP IN THE SCHOOL COLOURS.

By now Tufty and Scamp were regarded as bringers of bad luck. They were both sent packing.

BUZZ OFF WITH YOUR POOCH!

Next day Tufty went to the golf course where trials were being held for the school golf team.

PUT MY NAME DOWN, SIR!

RIGHT, TOWNSEND! BE READY TO START IN HALF AN HOUR.

Tufty lined up for his first drive.

WHACK! The ball swerved away over the bushes.

FORE!

OH, DEAR! THAT DOESN'T LOOK TOO PROMISING!

There was a mighty crash as the ball struck the windscreen of a parked car.

WOW!

The Games Master snatched the club.

YOU'RE NO USE, TOWNSEND! FRED FENTON WILL GET THE LAST PLACE IN THE SCHOOL TEAM.

Although not chosen to play, Tufty decided to follow Fred round the course with lucky mascot Scamp. It wasn't long before Fred hit a stray shot.

THE BALL WENT INTO THIS LONG GRASS!

Fred couldn't find the ball at all.

IF YOU CAN'T FIND YOUR BALL, I WILL WIN THE HOLE!

YOU GO LOOK FOR IT, SCAMP!

Scamp went zig-zagging into the long grass hunting this way and that. Soon he gave a sharp bark of discovery.

LOOK! SCAMP'S FOUND IT!

Fred took careful aim and lofted a super shot out of the rough to end up inches from the pin.

WHACKO! SUPER SHOT!

The Brampton lad played inspired golf after that. He won the match that helped gain the cup for the school.

WELL PLAYED, FENTON!

AND WELL DONE SCAMP, TOO!

Once again Tufty asked if he might celebrate with the winners.

MAY I JOIN IN THE CELEBRATION? AFTER ALL, SCAMP BROUGHT US LUCK.

NO! IT'S FOR PLAYERS ONLY!

On the way home, Tufty was spotted by Slugger Sloan and other toughs from the school which Brampton had beaten in the football match.

THERE'S ONE OF THE ROTTERS FROM BRAMPTON. LET'S BASH HIM!

Slugger galloped after Tufty and grabbed him by the scruff of the neck.

HEY! LEGGO!

Writhing and struggling, the two lads battled it out. Then as Slugger forced Tufty to the ground, Scamp leapt to help his master.

Slugger lashed out at Scamp and knocked the terrier headlong over the edge and into a rugged quarry.

CLEAR OFF, YOU BRUTE!

Slugger's cruelty roused Tufty to a fury. He leapt up and landed a terrific punch on Slugger's jaw.

TAKE THAT, YOU BULLY!

Tufty's schoolmates arrived in time to see that wallop, and they chased off Slugger and his henchmen.

SCAMP! ARE YOU ALL RIGHT?

Scamp wagged his tail away down on the floor of the quarry and Tufty picked his way down towards him.

IT'S OKAY, LADS! I'LL SOON FETCH HIM UP.

The terrier was none the worse for his fall. He bounded to clamber back up the slope with his master.

Halfway up, Scamp paused. He had found the entrance to a cave half hidden by undergrowth.

Scamp scuttled inside and began barking loudly.

WHAT'S UP, SCAMP?

Mystified, Tufty crept warily into the gloom.

GOSH! IT'S DARK IN HERE!

What an amazing treasure trove met the boy's eyes!

LOOK, LADS! SCAMP HAS FOUND ALL THE TROPHIES THAT WERE STOLEN FROM THE SCHOOL!

All the silverware was accounted for, and the boys carried it to the top of the quarry.

YOUR DOG SCAMP HAS BROUGHT US LOTS OF LUCK THIS TIME, TUFTY!

Tufty's pals had been most impressed by the punch that had sent Slugger reeling, and they persuaded him to enter for the inter-school boxing championships.

HONEST, SIR, TOWNSEND HAS GOT A KILLER PUNCH!

When the day of the contest came Tufty climbed into the ring and found his opponent was none other than Slugger Sloan.

WELL, I'M BLOWED! I'M UP AGAINST SLUGGER!

Slugger had a score to settle and began to biff Tufty about the head.

OUCH!

As the fight swayed to and fro, Tufty got trapped in a corner and was taking a terrific battering from Slugger.

COME ON, TUFTY!

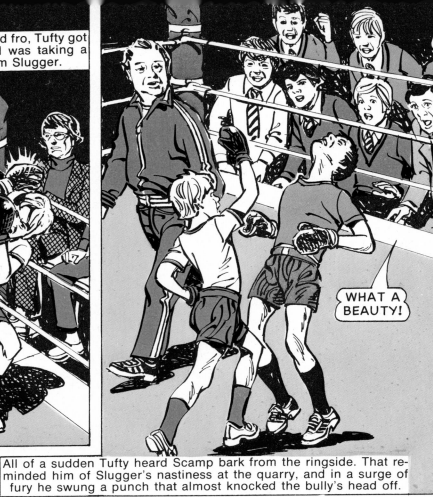

WHAT A BEAUTY!

All of a sudden Tufty heard Scamp bark from the ringside. That reminded him of Slugger's nastiness at the quarry, and in a surge of fury he swung a punch that almost knocked the bully's head off.

Slugger was counted out and Tufty was the champion.

EIGHT—NINE— TEN—OUT!

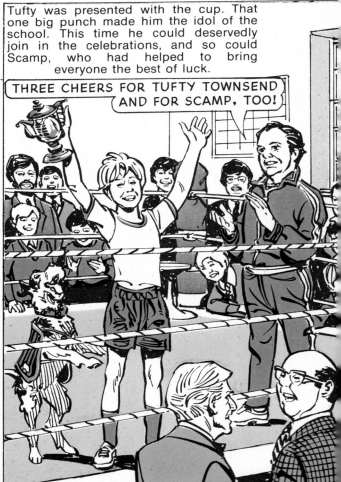

Tufty was presented with the cup. That one big punch made him the idol of the school. This time he could deservedly join in the celebrations, and so could Scamp, who had helped to bring everyone the best of luck.

THREE CHEERS FOR TUFTY TOWNSEND AND FOR SCAMP, TOO!

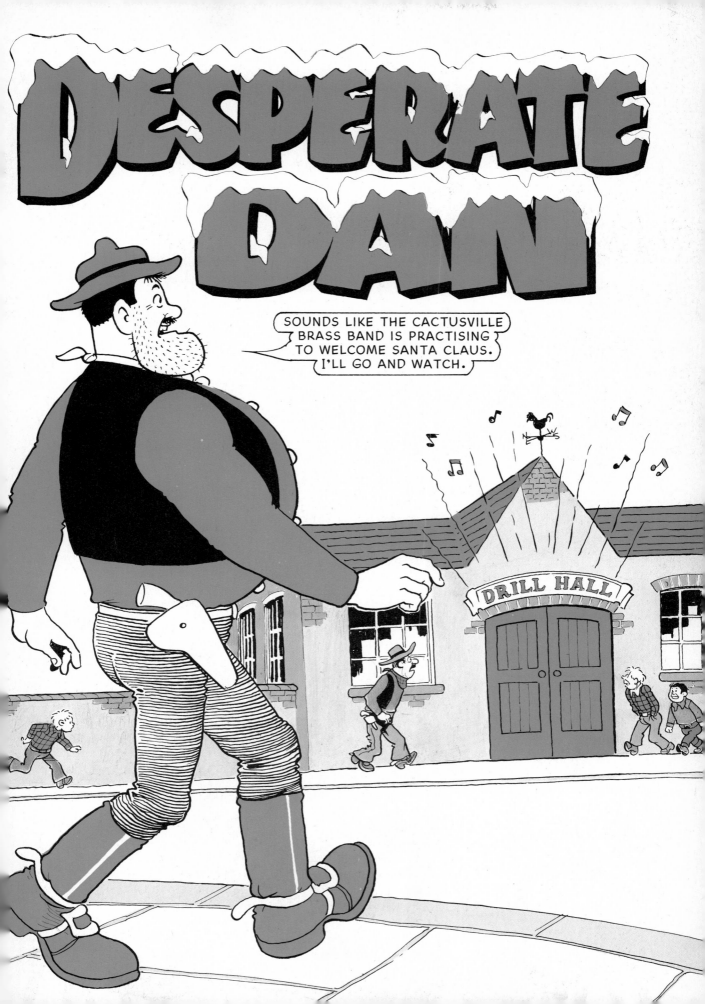

ZUNK!

IT WOULD BE BAD LUCK TO LOSE THAT SILVER DOLLAR! HELLO! WHAT'S HE JUMPING UP THERE FOR?

NOW LOOK WHAT YOU'VE DONE TO YOUR DRUM!

CRASH!

YOU BIG GALOOT! YOU'VE LAID OUT MY DRUMMER AND BUST HIS DRUM!

TAKE IT EASY, MISTER!

I'LL GET YOU A NEW DRUM AND A DRUMMER, TOO.

IN THE MUSIC SHOP—

A BIG DRUM, DAN? YOU MUST BE JOKING. THERE AIN'T NO SUCH THING AS A DRUM STRONG ENOUGH FOR YOU TO PLAY!

GEE! I CLEAN FORGOT THAT!

WHAT AM I GONNA DO? I'VE GOTTA GET A BIG DRUM SOMEHOW! SAY, THERE'S A PILLAR BOX! I WONDER—?

MUSIC

I'LL BORROW IT! GOOD JOB IT'S JUST BEEN EMPTIED.

# TOM TUM

HEE-HEE! I'VE SNAFFLED SOME GRUB FROM THE NEIGHBOUR'S PANTRY!

COME BACK, YOU PILFERING PEST!

**Later, two joiners arrive—**

I WANT YOU TO PUT AN EXTRA STRONG PADLOCK AND CHAIN ON MY PANTRY DOOR.

PANTRY

**Presently—**

GOSH! THAT MAKES THINGS DIFFICULT— BUT I'VE GOT A PLAN!

GOOD! TOM TUM HAS GOT A BIG PIE. THAT SHOULD KEEP HIM HAPPY FOR A WHILE!

TEE-HEE! NOW TO SNEAK INTO THE NEIGHBOUR'S HOUSE WHEN HE'S NOT LOOKING!

PANTRY

THIS IS A FAKE PIE! IT'S FULL OF WIRE-SNIPPERS AND OTHER TOOLS!

PANTRY

DONE IT!

SNIP!

OH, NO! AGAIN! HE'S EMPTIED MY PANTRY

TEAR! TEAR!

YUM-YUM! THIS WILL MAKE A TASTY SNACK!

ZOOM!

# A SUPER "ICE"

WHAT'S BETTER THAN A *NICE ICE*? I'LL TELL YOU— IT'S A *NICE ICE TWICE*! LOOK NOW AND SEE HOW MANY *ICES* ARE IN THE WORDS IN THOSE FIRST TWO SENTENCES. NO LESS THAN FIVE! AND LOTS MORE COMMONPLACE WORDS CONTAIN *ICE*. HERE IN WORDS AND IN PICTURES ARE CLUES TO SOME OF THEM. SEE HOW MANY YOU CAN PUZZLE OUT BEFORE LOOKING UP THE ANSWERS ON PAGE 141.

**1** THE GROCER PUTS THE HAM THROUGH THE _ _ _ _ _ _

**2** WHILE KORKY'S AWAY, WHO WILL PLAY? THE BILL _

**3** THE GAMEKEEPER IS PUTTING UP A WARNING _ _ _ _ _ _

**4** LOOK AT HIS BLACK MOUTH, AFTER HE'S BEEN EATING STICKY _ _ _ _ _ _ _ _

**5** THE SECRETARY WORKS IN A POSH _ _ _ _ _ _

**6** ARE LITTLE GIRLS REALLY MADE OF SUGAR AND SPICE?

**7** A BIG CRACK IN THE GROUND IS A _ _ _ _ _ _ _

**8** THIS GLASS OF _ _ _ _ _ REALLY HAS GOT ICE IN IT!

# SCREAM from KORKY

TO START A GAME OF SNAKES AND LADDERS ONE THROWS THE
DICE

10 ON THE RUN FROM AN ANGRY _____

11 THE NAME FOR MY BIG ARM MUSCLES IS _____

THIS JOINER'S _____ HAS A VERY STRONG GRIP.

13 WHICH APPLE DO YOU WANT? YOU HAVE A _____

GRANNY SMITHS    GOLDEN DELICIOUS

14 THE CITY OF _____ HAS LOTS OF CANALS.

SOLDIERS MUST ALWAYS SALUTE THEIR _____

16 THE CHINESE EAT LOTS OF RICE

17 THE SERGEANT HAS A VERY LOUD VOICE
ATTENTION!

THAT FISH IS CALLED _____

FRESH    NORMID

19 NOW LET ME GIVE YOU A WORD OF _____

20 £20 FOR A FOOTBALL! GOSH! WHAT A PRICE!

£15.00    £12.50    £20.00

1 TO BECOME A GOOD PLAYER YOU NEED LOTS OF _____

22 A BOY LEARNING A TRADE IS CALLED AN _____

23 THIS ICEBURG FLOATS IN THE ARCTIC OCEAN.

# The JOCKS and the GEORDIES

In a village on the Scottish Border are two schools, one on the Scottish side for the Jocks and another on the English side of the Border for the Geordies. When the two lots of school-boys meet, there are always fireworks, like when they go to the waxworks—

I'LL HANG THIS LIGHT UP HERE.

WHACK! WHACK!

OUCH! OUCH!

WHAT'S THAT BURNING SMELL?

SNIFF! SNIFF!

BLISTERING BLACKBOARDS! YOU'RE ON FIRE, BOY!

MOVE OUT OF THERE— HUH?

EEK! WHAT'S HAPPENED TO HIS LEG?

SWOON!

# Harry and his HIPPO

CRASH!
SHIVER!

DAD DOESN'T WANT YOU IN THE HOUSE, HIPPO. HE SAYS YOU HAVE TO SLEEP OUTSIDE.

SLAM!
ZZZZ

LEAP!
CRASH!
YIKE!

WHAT'S GOING ON? THE BRUTE'S BROKEN DOWN THE BACK DOOR AND WRECKED YOUR BED!
POOR OLD HIPPO! HE MUST HAVE BEEN FEELING THE COLD, DAD!

IF YOU BUILD A WARM KENNEL FOR HIM HE'LL BE ALL RIGHT OUTSIDE.
OKAY, I'LL BUILD ONE TOMORROW.

IT'S GOING TO BE BIG ENOUGH EVEN FOR HIPPO.

RIGHT, HIPPO! COME ON, IT'S TIME FOR BED.
GOODNIGHT, HARRY.

# Desperate DAWG

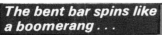

# JACK SILVER

ONE moment Curly Perkins was browsing quietly round a fantastic museum; the very next he was running like mad, for a huge Fuzzy Face with staring eyes had suddenly appeared in the doorway.

It was probably the weirdest of all the weird animals Curly had encountered since he arrived here in the wacky world of Marsuvia, far off in Outer Space, on a visit to his Marsuvian pal, Jack Silver.

The stabbing prongs had an astonishing effect on the animal. As Jack leaped down to follow Curly, the Fuzzy Face puffed out its cheeks and blew.

**ZAGH!** IT'S BLASTING OUT CLOUDS OF SOOT!

GASP!

The choking soot filled the whole big room, and the boys didn't know which way to turn to escape. The soot cleared, but the monster had gone.

AND LOOK! ALL THESE GOLD STATUES AND THINGS HAVE GONE TOO, JACK!

The chums dashed out of the museum with the attendant, but there was no sign of the Fuzzy Face.

THERE'S ZLOTTO AND HIS POOCHO! LET'S ASK IF HE SAW ANYTHING.

Jack told Zlotto what had happened, but the little chap was unable to help at all.

WHAT A FRIENDLY LITTLE POOCHO!

I SAW NOTHING COME OUT OF THE MUSEUM, JACK—AND MY POOCHO IS BLIND!

Jack and Curly were still chatting to Zlotto when a big van drew up beside them.

HEY, YOU, BOY! THAT POOCHO LOOKS AS IF IT CAN'T SEE!

THAT'S RIGHT. HE'S BLIND. SO WHAT?

The burly uniformed man snatched the old Poocho from its master.

ALL OLD AND USELESS PETS MUST BE PUT TO SLEEP. YOU KNOW THE LAW!

BUT HE'S NOT USELESS!

Curly Perkins decided he didn't like either this law or the man who was trying to enforce it. And he knew what to do about it!

YOU BIG BULLY! GO AND FETCH YOUR HAT!

HEY!

Quick as a flash, Curly snatched the Poocho's lead and ran for it. The queer dog was perhaps getting old, but it could still shake a leg!

COME BACK, YOU THIEVING RASCALS! I'LL CATCH YOU!

HO-HO! YOU'LL HAVE TO AIM YOUR LASSO GUN MORE CAREFULLY THAN THAT!

The boys easily outpaced the fat Poocho-catcher, and found a good hiding place for themselves.

QUICK, CURLY! DODGE IN HERE! HE'LL NEVER THINK OF LOOKING FOR US IN A BANK!

They got their breath back standing beside a huge fireplace in the bank.

WHAT'S THE POOCHO BARKING FOR? LOOK! THERE'S SOOT FALLING DOWN THE CHIMNEY!

Two seconds later, the boys and the Poocho jumped as a huge fuzzy sausage whooshed down the chimney.

AARGH! IT'S THAT MONSTER FROM THE MUSEUM!

ZOOYAH!

The bank customers were terrified as the monster turned itself back into a ball and puffed out another great sooty cloud.

DO SOMETHING, JACK! THERE'S GOING TO BE ANOTHER ROBBERY!

WHAT CAN I DO?

The sooty cloud billowed and swirled and engulfed the whole bank. Nobody could see a thing.

ZAIEE!

ZEEAGH!

The cloud cleared at last — and the boys saw at once that the robber had struck again.

ZOW! NOT A BANK NOTE LEFT! WE'VE BEEN CLEANED OUT!

ZASP! I GOT BIFFED!

Just then, the Poocho skipped up to Jack, drawn by the sound of his voice.

WHAT'S THAT YOU'VE GOT THERE, BOY? A PIECE OF BLUE CLOTH?

I BET IT COMES FROM THE ROBBER'S PANTS, JACK!

As Jack and Curly left the bank, they met a crowd of running people.

RUN FOR YOUR LIVES!

THE FUZZY FACE MUST HAVE STRUCK AGAIN, JACK!

IT'S HORRIBLE! ALL BLACK AND SOOTY!

The chums peered round the corner and what they saw made them gasp.

IT'S FLATTENING EVERYTHING IN THE STREET!

Suddenly the monster thumped down on to a moving car, then puffed out its cheeks and blew out yet another blast of soot.

WHAT'S THE IDEA? WHY HAS IT BLOWN A SOOT CLOUD ALONG THE STREET?

The answer to Jack's question was an almighty bang and the sound of splintering glass.

ZOWEE! LISTEN TO THAT! THE SOOTY CLOUD HAS CAUSED A TRAFFIC ACCIDENT!

Before Jack could do anything, the Poocho leaped forward into the thick cloud.

HEY! COME BACK! DON'T GO IN THERE!

The chums groped their way into the dense cloud to seek the blind Poocho.

When the sooty cloud began to clear, the boys saw that the street was jammed with wreckage. Several vehicles had piled into each other.

WE WERE CARRYING VALUABLE JEWELLERY. OUR VAN BURST OPEN IN THE CRASH AND WE DIDN'T EVEN SEE WHO ROBBED US!

SECURUM

GOSH!

But then the Poocho hopped up to Jack again.

REMEMBER THAT HE'S BLIND! THE SOOTY CLOUD MAKES NO DIFFERENCE TO HIM!

ANOTHER SCRAP OF BLUE CLOTH! HOW DID YOU GET IT?

Next moment, Jack spotted the Fuzzy Face up to more mischief.

LOOK! LET'S GET AFTER IT! COME ON, POOCHO!

Jack snapped out orders to the Poocho this time!

SEEK OUT THE ROBBER, POOCHO! SEEK!

The blind Poocho dashed into the billowing and choking blackness.

Jack and Curly listened hard, and heard loud yells from inside the cloud.

ZAGH! NOT YOU AGAIN! GERROFF, YOU BRUTE!

Ten seconds later, the Poocho reappeared.

YOU'VE DONE IT AGAIN, POOCHO! THE ROBBER WILL SOON HAVE NO PANTS LEFT!

The chums took the scraps of cloth along to the police station. Jack felt there was something familiar about them.

I'M SURE I KNOW WHO THE ROBBER IS—AND I THINK I KNOW HOW TO CATCH HIM!

And so, some time later a security guard left one of the city's banks with a gold shipment, accompanied only by Jack, Curly and the Poocho.

BE CAREFUL WITH THAT BULLION NOW!

BANK

It was asking for trouble, and trouble came along quickly — in the shape of the big Fuzzy Face.

LOOK OUT, JACK!

ZOW! I KNOW WHAT'S GOING TO HAPPEN NEXT!

Jack was right. The monster puffed out its cheeks and blasted a dense cloud around the bullion van.

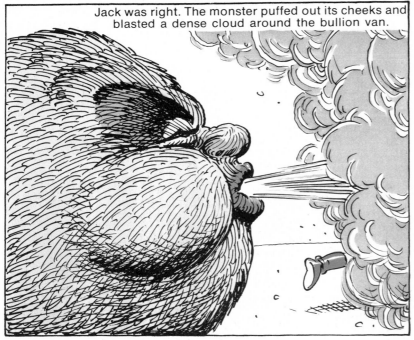

But Jack Silver was ready this time!

QUICK! SWITCH ON NOW!

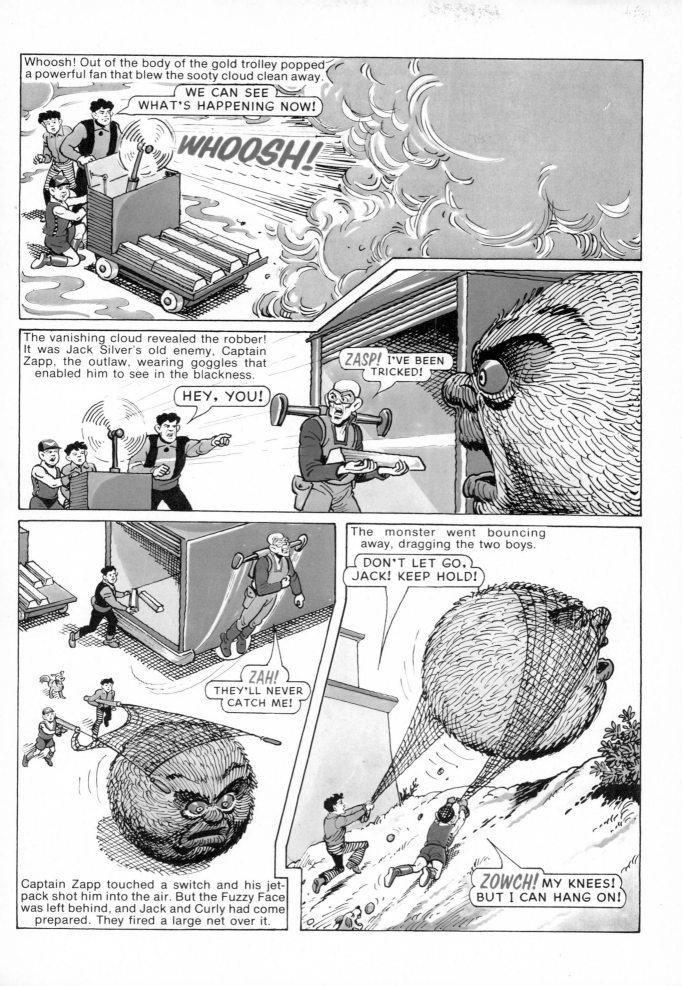

The boys were scraped and bumped and banged along the ground, but they hung on grimly until they were dragged, panting for breath, into a woodland clearing.

LOOK! IT'S BROUGHT US TO WHERE CAPTAIN ZAPP'S SPACESHIP IS PARKED!

SO IT HAS!

Captain Zapp was loading up with the loot from his other robberies, but he whirled round when he heard his monster approaching.

YOU IDIOT! YOU'VE BETRAYED ME BY BRINGING ALONG THESE BRATS!

Wild with rage, Captain Zapp drew his blaster gun and fired.

GET THESE SPIES AWAY FROM HERE, YOU FUZZY FREAK!

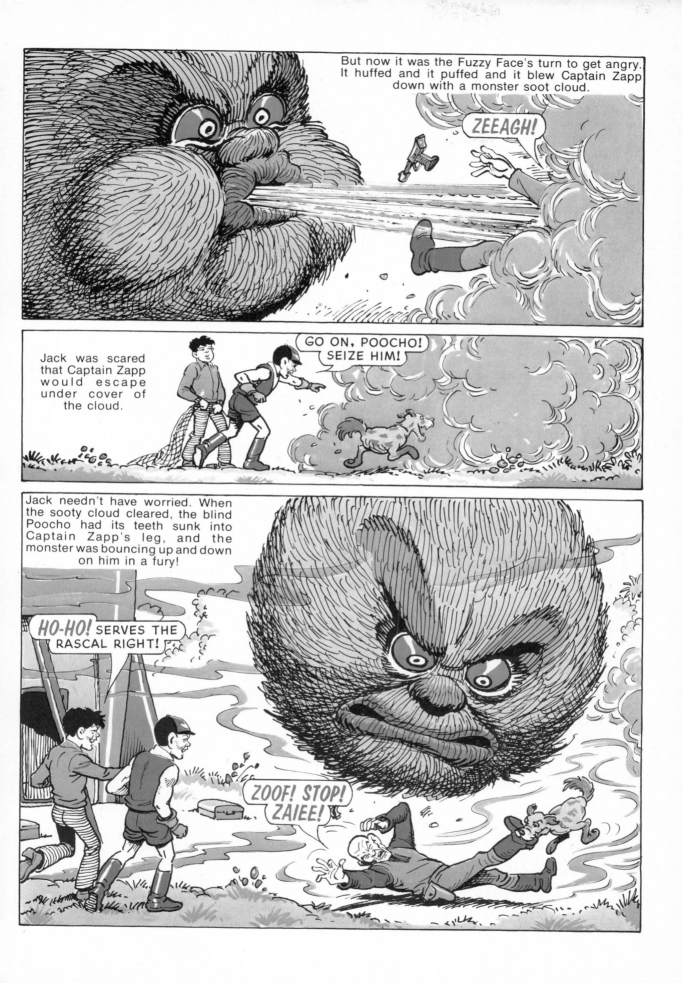

The monster at last gave up pounding the scoundrel and bounced off. But Captain Zapp was too dazed to resist arrest.

IT'S JAIL FOR YOU, BALDY!

AND WE'VE SEEN THE LAST OF THE FUZZY FACE. LOOK AT IT GO!

Every single piece of loot was recovered, and praises were heaped upon the gallant Poocho. But he was certainly in need of a bath after dashing in and out of so many clouds of soot!

ZAW-HAW! HE'S BEING PAMPERED LIKE A PRINCE!

Little Zlotto's Poocho had proved beyond doubt that it was still very far from useless. In fact, instead of having it put to sleep, the Mayor awarded it a special medal!

THANKS FOR SAVING MY POOCHO, JACK AND CURLY!

ZAW-HAW! IT'S CAPTAIN ZAPP YOU SHOULD THANK, BUT HE'S BEHIND BARS!

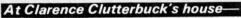

# TOM TUM

*At Clarence Clutterbuck's house—*

AND NOW CLARENCE WILL LET YOU HEAR SOME OF HIS FAVOURITE TAPE-RECORDINGS.

THIS IS A LOVELY PIECE OF BALLET MUSIC.

BAH! WHAT A LOAD OF SOPPY JUNK!

TRA-LA-LA!

PERHAPS YOU WOULD LIKE TO BORROW MY OLD TAPE-RECORDER? YOU'LL GET LOTS OF FUN FROM IT.

OH, ER! YES, THANKS!

*Later—*

AH! I'VE GOT AN IDEA!

ZOO

ROAR!

I'LL TAPE A LION'S ROAR.

MONKEYS

NOW TO VISIT THE MONKEY HOUSE.

HEE-HEE! JUST AS I HOPED. THAT ROAR HAS SCARED THE MONKEYS OUT OF THEIR WITS AND MADE THEM DROP THEIR BANANAS!

CLICK!

ROAR!

YUM-YUM! SUPER GRUB!

CHOMP!

MONKEYS

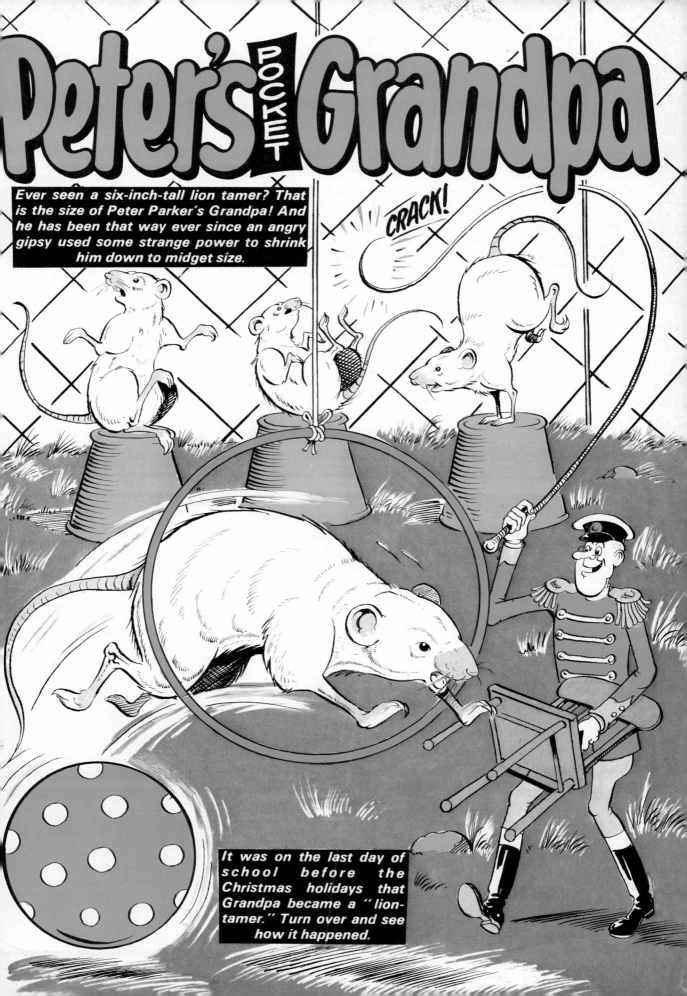

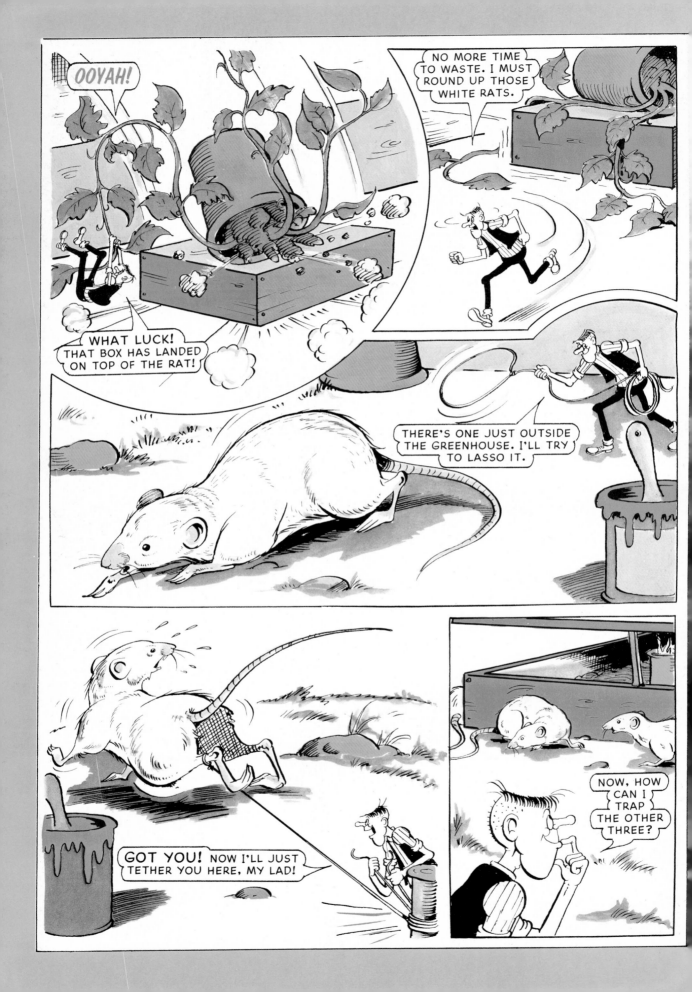

THESE BITS OF CHEESE I'VE BROUGHT OUT WILL MAYBE LURE THEM INTO DAD'S GARDEN FRAME.

IT'S WORKING! WATCH THIS!

JUST ONE GOOD SWIPE—!

SLAM!

CRACK!

AND THE LID DROPS DOWN AND TRAPS THEM. I CAN GO AND SEE PETER NOW!

OH, HELLO, GRANDPA. THAT BOX OF MINE HAS THE SCHOOL'S WHITE RATS IN IT. I'VE BEEN ASKED TO LOOK AFTER THEM DURING THE HOLIDAYS.

I—ER—FOUND THEM, PETER!

GRANDPA! WHAT A MESS!

OH, DEAR! THE STUPID ANIMAL HAS KNOCKED OVER AN OLD POT OF PAINT!

# KORKY'S GALLERY

CAPTAIN COOK MADE THREE VOYAGES ROUND THE WORLD. HE WAS KILLED DURING THE FIRST OF THESE.

JAMES COOK

A PARADOX IS A CROSS BETWEEN A PARROT AND AN OX.

WHO'S A PRETTY BOY, THEN?

SILLY MOOO!

NELSON SAID — ENGLAND EXPECTS EVERY MAN TO PAY HIS DUTY.

COUGH UP, ME HEARTIES!

COUGH COUGH

BACCY-DUTY FREE PAYABLE

IN SPRING THE LAMBS CAN BE SEEN GAMBLING IN THE FIELDS.

IN SOME BUSES THEY HAVE SMOKING ALOUD.

SUCK PUFF CRACKLE HISS

A SCHOOLBOY HOWLER IS A SIX FOOT CANE.

HOWL! WHACK! WHACK! SWISH!

THE DOCTOR FELT HIS PATIENT'S PURSE.

TICK TICK

OH, DEAR! NO CHANGE!

AUGUST 27th. WAS KING ALFRED'S BATHDAY.

A SIREN IS A DANGEROUS WOMAN SOMETIMES FOUND IN A FACTORY.

MOAN!

GUERRILLA WARFARE IS WHERE THE TROOPS ARE CLOSE ENOUGH TO MAKE FACES AT EACH OTHER.

YAH! BOO!

FISH-FACE!

UGLY MUGS!

FAT NOSED BABOONS!

A LAWSUIT IS THE UNIFORM WORN BY POLICEMEN.

SWAG

# of SCHOOLBOY HOWLERS

A CURVE IS THE LONGEST DISTANCE BETWEEN TWO POINTS.

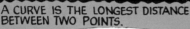

CHARLES THE FIRST DIED OF EXCITEMENT WHEN HE LOST HIS HEAD.

I HAVE FOUND IT, SIRE!

TOO LATE — THE EXCITEMENT WAS TOO MUCH FOR HIM!

GOOSEBERRIES ARE GRAPES WITH HAIRS ON.

MOTHER SENT THEM, DEAR!

THE OPPOSITE OF NEGATIVE IS PHOTOGRAPH.

IS THAT A PICTURE OF YOU, MY DEAR?

THE ANSWER IS IN THE NEGATIVE!

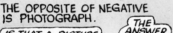

AN OBOE IS AN AMERICAN TRAMP WHO PLAYS IN A B.B.C. DANCE BAND.

THE HIGHWAY CODE IS A BOOK OF RULES FOR WALKERS WHO ARE RUN OVER.

DAZE

READ THIS!

A NIGHTWATCHMAN IS A MAN EMPLOYED TO SLEEP IN THE OPEN AIR.

ZZZ

ROAD

DOCTORS NOW TREAT THEIR PATIENTS WITH ULTRA VIOLENT RAYS.

YAHOO!

POLITICS IS WHEN A PARROT SWALLOWS A WATCH.

TICK-TICK
TICK-TICK

ROBERT LOUIS STEVENSON DIED OF A VERY PAINFUL MELODY.

SCREECH

THE CRUSADES WERE WHEN THE CHRISTIANS FOUGHT THE TURKEYS.

GOBBLE
GOBBLE
GOBBLE

GRAVITY IS A LAW HOLDING THINGS UP BUT NOWADAYS WE USE ELASTIC.

OH, NO!

PING

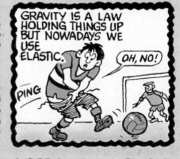

WILLIAM TELL SHOT AN ARROW THROUGH AN APPLE WHEN STANDING ON HIS SON'S HEAD.

TWANG!

HOI!

ORCHARD KEEP OUT.

GOOD SHOT, DAD!

THE ROMANS DROVE THE PIXIES OVER HADRIAN'S WALL.

HADRIAN'S PLACE.

HEY! WHAT GOES ON?

HI, HADRIAN!

# GREEDY PIGG

WHAT LUCK! COOK HAS LEFT A BIG CUSTARD TART CLOSE TO THE WINDOW. I'LL HAVE IT!

HO-HO! THAT'S NOT A CUSTARD TART, IT'S A MUSTARD TART! I MADE IT SPECIALLY FOR PIGGY TO STEAL.

PIGGY'S GRABBED A TART FROM THE SCHOOL KITCHEN. THIS ROPE WILL HELP ME PINCH IT FROM HIM!

A CUSTARD TART! THANK YOU VERY MUCH, PIGGY!

TUG!

ERK!

LOOK WHAT JASPER'S GOT! C'MON, LADS, WE'LL FIX UP A LITTLE SURPRISE FOR HIM IN HIS WORKSHOP.

I CAN SCOFF THE TART IN PEACE IN HERE.

A PRESENT FOR ME! TA, JASPER!

CLUNK!

GURR! COME BACK, YOU YOUNG SCAMPS!

HURRAY! A BIG CUSTARD TART!

# Bertie Buncle
## and his chemical uncle

FIRST I HAVE TO INSERT A TINY SIGNALLING GADGET INTO EACH BALL.

THAT'S CLEVER, UNCLE BUNCLE. YOU'VE EVEN INVENTED A SPECIAL TOOL TO GET IT INTO THE BALL!

[I']M FED UP LOSING GOLF BALLS [O]UT ON THE GOLF COURSE. THIS [N]EW MACHINE I'VE INVENTED WILL [P]UT AN END TO THAT!

GOSH! IT LOOKS LIKE A SPOTTED DOG, UNCLE!

HERE GOES FOR THE FIRST TEST. SEE! MY BALL HAS CURLED AWAY INTO THE BUSHES!

[B]UT THERE GOES MY BALLSEEKER! LET'S FOLLOW HIM AND SEE HOW HE DOES.

SURE!

LOOK AT THAT! HE'S FOUND IT FIRST TIME!

BRILLIANT!

OH, BOY! I'LL SNEAK OFF WITH THE BALLSEEKER AND HAVE SOME SUPER FUN WITH IT!

[I']LL JUST SLIP ONE OF UNCLE'S [S]IGNALLING GOLF BALLS INTO TEACHER'S POCKET.

NOW TO STAND BACK AND WATCH THE FUN. THERE GOES THE BALLHOUND!

# IZZY SKINT
## HE ALWAYS IS!

IT'S NO FUN WALKING ROUND A FAIRGROUND WHEN YOU'RE SKINT, SAM.

YOU'RE RIGHT, IZZY!

PERFORMING DOGS! THAT GIVES ME A GOOD IDEA.

ENTRY 50p

MARVO AND HIS PERFORMING DOGS

IF I COULD TEACH OUR BONGO TO PERFORM TRICKS, PEOPLE MIGHT PAY ME TO COME AND SEE HIM!

I DOUBT IT VERY MUCH!

I'LL START TRAINING BONGO RIGHT AWAY.

C'MON, BOY! I WANT YOU TO JUMP THROUGH THIS HOOP.

HURRY UP, BONGO. JUMP THROUGH THE HOOP— HE'S NOT BUDGING!

BAH!

THAT BONE MIGHT MAKE BONGO CHANGE HIS MIND.

HE'LL JUMP THROUGH THE HOOP TO GET AT THE BONE.

HERE, BONGO, A JUICY BONE FOR YOU!

# THE SMASHER

'M STARVING, SO I'LL "BORROW" SOME BISCUITS.

WHAT WAS THAT NOISE? IS THAT YOU, SMASHER?

MUM SOUNDS ANGRY! I'M OFF!

I'LL TRY SNEAKING SOME GRUB FROM THE PANTRY.

SHOVE

SWING

OOPS! NO WONDER I'M CALLED SMASHER!

BUMP!

SMASH!

GURR! WAS THAT YOU TRYING TO STEAL SOME FOOD?

ME, MUM? MUST HAVE BEEN THE WIND!

GROAN! I'M STILL HUNGRY!

HEY, SMASHER! HOW ABOUT US PLAYING COPS AND ROBBERS?

OKAY, BILLY.

YOU GO INTO MY HOUSE, FILL A BASKET WITH GRUB—AND I'LL BE THE COP.

ER . . .

SHOVE

I HOPE SMASHER'S MUM DOESN'T CATCH ME ROBBING THIS "BANK"!

STOP, ROBBER!

WHAT'S THAT? A ROBBER?

GOOD LAD, SMASHER!

GRAB!

WELL DONE, SON! YOU DESERVE SOME GRUB AS A REWARD!

THANKS, DAD.

COME HERE, YOU LITTLE THIEF!

HUH! CRAFTY OLD SMASHER! NOW I KNOW WHY HE LET ME BE THE ROBBER!

MUNCH! CHOMP!

# HERE'S A HOOT!

WHAT'S FUNNY ABOUT A *BOWL* WITH AN *OWL* IN IT? NOTHING MAYBE—EXCEPT THAT THERE ARE TWO *OWLS* IN THAT FIRST SENTENCE. THERE'S ONE IN THAT WORD *BOWL*, YOU SEE!
AND IT'S SURPRISING HOW MANY OTHER WORDS HAVE AN *OWL* IN THEM. SEE FOR YOURSELF WHEN YOU TRY THIS GAME. EVERY PICTURE GIVES A CLUE TO A WORD WITH AN *OWL* IN IT. PUZZLE THEM OUT AND DON'T LOOK UP THE ANSWERS (*ON PAGE 141*) UNTIL YOU'VE FOUND THEM ALL.

**1** MIDNIGHT _____

**2** A PAINTER USES A _____ TO REMOVE PAINT.

**3** THE APPLE PIE IS SITTING ON THE WINDOW _____

**4** A _____ OF SOIL.

**5** A TORTOISE WALKS VERY _____

**6** "HOWZAT?" SHOUTS THE _____

CLICK

**7** IN SCOTLAND SOME PEOPLE VISIT THE HIGHLANDS AND SOME VISIT THE _____

# SPOT THE "OWL"!

**8** HE HAS A \_\_\_\_\_ ON HIS FACE!

**9** THESE TWO CARS ARE FIXED TOGETHER BY A _____

**10** A \_\_\_\_\_ OF FRUIT.

**11** IF I STICK A PIN IN HIS PANTS, THAT WILL MAKE HIM \_\_\_\_

**12** THE SHAPE OF THIS COWBOY'S LEGS.

**13** THE SOUND A WOLF MAKES.

**14** FOUND IN THE FARMYARD.

**15** A HAT WORN BY A CITY GENT.

**16** THEY'RE PLAYING A GAME OF \_\_\_\_\_

**17** THE ARCHER HAS MISSED THE TARGET VERY _____

TWANG!

**18** WHO INVENTED FRACTIONS, BOY?
HENRY THE EIGHTH, SIR.
AN EXAMPLE OF A SCHOOLBOY _____

**19** YOU'LL LEARN A LOT FROM THIS BOOK OF _____
ENCYCLOPEDIA

**20** DON'T ANNOY THE DOG OR HE'LL \_\_\_\_\_
GRRRR

# BRASSNECK

CHARLEY BRAND was the lad with the most amazing pal in the world. Brassneck was an all-metal boy, with cog and spring innards and an electric brainbox. He could walk and talk and do all the things any boy could do — and lots more besides. He could even ride a horse and make it go like the wind. Read on and see how it all happened.

DUNWORKIN

Brassneck's tremendous adventure began on the day when Dad Brand took the whole family to a country fair. Brassneck and Charley had great fun and Mum and Dad, too, enjoyed it no end.

WOULDN'T MIND WINNING A LIVE PIG OR A BARREL OF CIDER! I'LL TAKE A TICKET IN BRASSNECK'S NAME. HE'S GOT LOADS OF LUCK!

METAL PEST! CAN'T YOU MISS JUST ONCE?

LOOK AT BRASSNECK, MUM! HE'S A DEAD SHOT.

GRAND RAFFLE
SUPER LIST OF PRIZES

At the end of the day they went home on the bus as happy as larks, with large ice creams and an armful of coconuts.

SHOULDN'T WE HAVE STAYED FOR THE RAFFLE DRAW, DAD?

NO NEED! IF BRASSNECK WINS, THE PRIZE WILL BE DELIVERED.

KISS ME QUICK

I LOVE ME

I LOVE LUDO

They were sitting at their supper when there came a knock at the door.

MAYBE SOMEBODY'S COME TO DELIVER MY PRIZE!

HO-HO! WHAT AN OPTIMIST YOU ARE, BRASSNECK!

But it was indeed a man from the fair, and he wanted to know if Brassneck Brand lived at this address.

WHY, YES, HE DOES.

GOOD. HE'S WON A SUPER PRIZE. HERE, GRAB THIS ROPE!

Dad was left blinking at the rope in his hands.

WHAT KIND OF A PRIZE IS THIS?

He gave the rope a tug, and next moment a very large head poked its way round the door.

EEK!

A HORSE!

He wasn't the most handsome horse in the world, but one person fell in love with him at first sight.

THAT UGLY BRUTE WILL GO RIGHT BACK TO THE FAIR!

NO, HE WON'T! THIS IS MY HORSE! NOT YOURS!

But Dad was just as determined and furious, too!

GET RID OF IT, I TELL YOU!

LOOK WHAT YOU'VE DONE! MADE ME HIT THE HORSE!

The indignant horse whirled around and hoofed Brassneck in the midriff.

BLEEK!

HOI! WATCH IT!

And that kick knocked Brassneck's works wonky. He would not listen to Dad's commands or to Charley's pleading. He would keep that horse, come what may!

I'LL TETHER LIGHTNING HERE IN THE GARDEN FOR THE NIGHT. AND I'LL GUARD HIM AND BASH ANYONE WHO DARES TO TOUCH HIM!

GROAN! BRASSNECK'S GONE BATTY!

There was nothing else for it but to go to bed. Charley awoke early in the morning and looked anxiously out.

YAWN—OH, GOOD GRIEF! MR CRUMP'S GARDEN!

Greedy Lightning had eaten everything in the Brands' garden, then chewed his way through the hedge and cropped as much as he could reach of all that grew in the neighbour's garden.

AARGH! MY APPLE TREE! EATEN BARE!

It was more than Mr Crump could take. He rushed indoors and snatched up the first weapon he saw — a big frying pan.

GET OUT OF HERE, YOU MONSTER!

But as Mr Crump's pan crashed down, Brassneck's head popped up. CLANG!

LEAVE MY LIGHTNING ALONE, YOU BIG BULLY!

CLANG!

Dad surveyed the damage to his neighbour's property. His own garden looked as though ten million caterpillars had held a banquet there!

WHERE HAVE YOU BEEN? WHY HAVEN'T YOU BEEN HERE MAKING SURE THAT FOUR-LEGGED MINCER DIDN'T MINCE UP EVERYTHING THAT GROWS?

I WAS AWAY GETTING LIGHTNING SOME FOOD!

ER...YOU DROPPED YOUR HAT, MR CRUMP.

Off rushed Brassneck, to return moments later carrying half a haystack from round the corner.

SEE! I BROUGHT ENOUGH TO KEEP LIGHTNING GOING.

HURRY UP, YOU FOOL, BEFORE HE EATS THE JERSEY OFF MY BACK!

Next thing an angry farmer appeared. It seems he had followed the trail of hay all the way from his farm.

THAT HAY WAS TAKEN WITHOUT PERMISSION— SO PAY UP!

YOU'VE DONE IT NOW, BRASSNECK!

I DON'T CARE! LIGHTNING IS HUNGRY!

And, of course, Mr Crump wanted payment for his damaged garden.

IF THIS KEEPS UP, I'LL BE BROKE INSIDE TEN MINUTES!

For the next few days Brassneck kept his horse in hiding and the crafty metal lad made a muzzle for him to keep his appetite in check. Brassneck figured that Lightning was too heavy with food to be able to jump.

Charley tracked Brassneck down eventually by following the trail of broken gates and flattened fences.

But Brassneck had a surprise in store for Charley. He had spent lots of time teaching Lightning to jump.

Then Brassneck leaped on to Lightning's back.

By the end of the day Brassneck had Lightning leaping like a grasshopper all over the countryside.

Brassneck persuaded Charley to bring another bucketful of milk and eggs along to the Midtown racetrack and give Lightning a whiff of it.

THAT'S FOR YOU, BOY— AT THE END OF THE RACE!

Now Brassneck turned the horse and rode him all the way round the track to the starting gates, with Lightning looking back longingly at the bucket.

I'LL TAKE YOUR MUZZLE OFF SOON, LIGHTNING.

In fact, that was the last thing Brassneck did before remounting at the starting gates.

HURRY UP! YOU'RE HOLDING UP THE RACE!

The gates were opened. And they were off! And the eager Lightning bolted into the lead like a shot from a gun!

Lightning cleared the first fence ahead of every other horse.

GO, BOY—GO!

Never had anyone seen a horse race so fast! The other jockeys saw only his clean pair of heels all the way round the track.

GASP! THAT ONE'S GOING LIKE STEAM!

The winning post! Lightning streaked towards it with his eyes fixed upon the bucket beyond it. Crafty Brassneck had known how to make the horse live up to his name!

GO GET IT, BOY!

WHAT A HORSE!

COME ON, LIGHTNING! HERE'S YOUR GRUB!

And that's how Brassneck and Lightning won the Midtown Steeplechase.

NOW YOU'LL COME HOME, BRASSNECK, WON'T YOU?

But that's not the end of the tale. You see, although Dad had no love for Lightning, Mum certainly had, and she had risked a whole pound on him.

RESULTS

1 LIGHTNING 100/1
2 FERRY BOY 7/2
3 JUNIOR JIM 3/1

GRACIOUS ME! IT'S LIGHTNING! I'VE WON A HUNDRED POUNDS!

Brassneck and Lightning were made very welcome back home — especially by Dad!

I ALWAYS SAID HE WAS A CHAMPION HORSE!

While Charley repaired Brassneck's upset works, Dad Brand cleared out the garden shed.

I'M TURNING THE SHED INTO A STABLE FOR LIGHTNING.

That night there was a smashing party in the Brand household. The winnings had paid for all the damage and left plenty over to buy loads of party fare. And Dad sang all the horsey songs he knew.

A FOUR-LEGGED FRIEND!

YES, A FOUR-LEGGED FRIEND!

But next morning, when Dad looked out the window . . .

GOOD GRIEF!

Lightning had done it again! During the night he had broken out of his stable and crashed through the fence into the next garden. There he had eaten all the choicest fruit and vegetables — and he was still at it!

BRAND! COME OUT HERE! LOOK WHAT YOUR NAG HAS DONE!

Cruncher Caine, the champion wrestler, was the owner. Poor Dad didn't dare argue with him.

THAT HORSE IS A BLOOMIN' WRECKER! IT HAS GOT TO GO!

Y-Y-YES, MR CAINE!

In spite of the joy Lightning had brought them yesterday, the whole Brand family realised that it was just not possible to keep a horse in their back garden — and especially not one with Lightning's appetite.

TAKE IT EASY, BRASSNECK. WE REALLY CAN'T KEEP YOUR HORSE.

Lightning was sold that same day, and Brassneck and Charley made fond farewells to the world's hungriest horse while Dad counted the loot.

OO! WHAT A LOT OF MONEY!

WE'LL LOOK AFTER HIM VERY WELL—AND YOU CAN ALWAYS VISIT LIGHTNING.

GOODBYE, OLD CHUM!

The money from the sale paid for all the damage. And it also bought Mum a new rig-out, Dad a barrel of cider, and Charley a bucket of ice cream. As for Brassneck, the retired jockey could now afford to dress like a lord every day of the week!

YOU'RE THE BEST AND LUCKIEST PAL I EVER HAD, BRASSNECK!

ICE CREAM

# Greedy PIGG

**Mr Pigg:** I'M A FINE COOK, HEADMASTER. I CAN FIX UP LUNCH FOR THE BOYS.

**Headmaster:** THAT'S VERY HELPFUL OF YOU, MR PIGG.

**Headmaster:** OH, DEAR! THE COOK'S ILL AND CAN'T COME IN TO COOK THE LUNCH TODAY. WHAT CAN WE DO?

**Mr Pigg:** I'M COOK TODAY, BOYS. I HOPE YOU ENJOY MY COOKING.

**Boy:** BAH! WHAT TINY HELPINGS!

**Boy:** NOT ENOUGH TO FEED A MOUSE!

LOOK, JASPER! PIGGY'S LOCKED HIMSELF IN THE KITCHEN TO SCOFF ALL THE GRUB WE SHOULD HAVE GOT FOR LUNCH!

THAT TABLE HAS METAL CASTERS. I KNOW HOW TO MAKE USE OF THEM!

I'M RIGHT UNDER WHERE PIGGY IS AND THIS STRONG MAGNET WILL PLAY TRICKS WITH HIS TABLE!

I'LL START WITH THE PIE.

ERK!

THE TABLE MUST HAVE ROLLED DOWN A SLOPE ON THE FLOOR! I'LL MOVE MY STOOL OVER THERE.

ERK! THE TABLE'S MOVED AGAIN!

I'LL GET A HAMMER AND NAIL THE TABLE DOWN TO STOP IT ROLLING.

SCHOOL KITCHEN

HERE HE COMES NOW, LADS!

THAT'S ENOUGH POLISH, PERCY. I'LL PUT THE MAT DOWN AGAIN.

POLISH

I'D BETTER HURRY BEFORE ANYONE SEES ALL MY GRUB AND SCOFFS THE LOT!

WHAT ON EARTH? I'M SLIPPING!

GOT HIM! NOW I'LL SLAM THE DOOR.

WHOOSH!

HEE-HEE! THAT'S PIGGY SAFELY LOCKED AWAY!

BAH! LET ME OUT OF HERE!

SOME HOPES!

BROOM CUPBOARD

PIGGY OUGHT TO BE PLEASED TO KNOW WE'RE ALL ENJOYING HIS SPLENDID COOKING. HEE-HEE!

# The JOCKS and the GEORDIES

In a great tale of Flying Saucers—and flying fists!

**Back at the Geordies' hut—**

IS THAT SO? THEN WE'LL MAKE SURE THEY SEE A FLYING SAUCER TONIGHT, LADS!

HA-HA! WE'LL SOON HAVE OUR MASTERPIECE FINISHED.

SNIP! SNIP!

PASTE

**That night—**

SPOT ANYTHING, ECK?

NOT A THING— EXCEPT A GEORDIE RUNNING THIS WAY!

I CLAIM FIRST THUMP AT HIM!

WHEEZE! WAIT, JOCKS! I'D RATHER BE WITH YOU THAN NEAR THAT THING IN THE FIELD!

WHAT THING? TELL US—OR WE'LL BIFF YOU!

A FLYING SAUCER, THAT'S WHAT. ON THE COMMON!

WE'RE NOT FRIGHTENED OF IT. COME ON, JOCKS!

THAT NEWS ABOUT THE FLYING SAUCER HAS SAVED YOU FROM A BASHING, GEORDIE!

IT-IT'S A BIT S-SPOOKY OUT HERE, B-BIG JOCK!

N-NO SIGN OF THE S-SAUCER. ER, LET'S G-GO HOME THEN!

STAY HERE, JOCKS! IF WE SPOT IT, WE'LL BECOME FAMOUS, REMEMBER!

EEK! DEATH RAYS! RUN!

HELP!

WAAH!

**Next day—**

—AND THEN THEY TURNED THEIR DEATH RAYS ON US AND WE JUST GOT AWAY IN TIME!

QUITE A STORY, BUT YOU NEED PROOF—A PHOTO OR A PIECE OF THE SAUCER!

TEACHER'S RIGHT! WE NEED PROOF. WE'LL GO BACK TO THE COMMON TONIGHT!

GULP! WE WILL?

**After school—**

GO HOME AND FETCH YOUR CAMERA, ECK.

OH, ALL RIGHT, BUT I STILL DON'T LIKE THE IDEA!

**On the way to the Jocks' hut—**

THEATRE

WE'LL BORROW THESE SPACEMEN COSTUMES FOR TONIGHT, AND PUT THE WIND UP THE JOCKS AGAIN!

GOSH! SO IT WAS THE GEORDIES! I'LL HAVE TO TELL BIG JOCK THAT WE'VE BEEN TRICKED!

OKAY, JOCKS! WE'LL SURPRISE THOSE GEORDIE ROTTERS IN OUR OWN SPACEMEN COSTUMES AND THEY'RE THE ONES WHO'LL BE FRIGHTENED! GET BUSY, JOCKS!

THE TRICKS OF → **SCREWY DRIVER**

**GOSH!** IT'S SNOWING HARD. HOW WILL I GET TO WORK TOMORROW?

LEAVE THAT TO ME, DAD!

I'LL NEED THE ENGINE FROM THE MOTOR MOWER...

*Next day—*

COME ON, DAD! I'VE MADE A MOTOR SLEDGE. I'LL START UP BEFORE YOU CLIMB ABOARD.

**YEEAGH!** IT'S SHOWERING ME WITH SNOW! **STOP IT, SCREWY!**

EH?

WHOOSH!

**BAH!** YOU'D BETTER DESIGN A SAFER MACHINE—AND HURRY UP WITH IT!

YES, DAD!

GET A MOVE ON, SCREWY! I'M GOING TO BE LATE!

NEARLY READY!

THERE! INSTEAD OF A PADDLE, IT'S GOT A PROPELLER NOW.

STILL DOESN'T LOOK SAFE TO ME!

**OOPS!** I'VE HIT THE EDGE OF A SNOWY BANK!

**AARGH!** WE'RE BEING THROWN OFF! **HELP!**

# Desperate DAWG

HEY! YOU'RE SUPPOSED TO BE KEEPING THE PEACE WHILE THE SHERIFF'S AWAY, DESPERATE DAWG. IT'S YOUR JOB TO SILENCE THESE ROWDIES!

I HAVE AN IDEA—BUT I'LL HAVE TO BORROW THE TOWN HALL BELL FOR IT.

TOWN HALL

BANG!

BANG!

YIPPEE!

BANG! BANG! BANG! BANG!

YOO-HA!

HOI! WHAT'S GOING ON?

BONG! BONG!

YOW! AAGH!

HA-HA! THAT SHOULD TEACH 'EM THAT SILENCE IS GOLDEN!

RRRRRING!

NOW I'LL TAKE THIS BACK TO THE TOWN HALL.

DAGNAB IT! IT'S CAUGHT ON TO SOMETHING.

CRACK!

BONG!

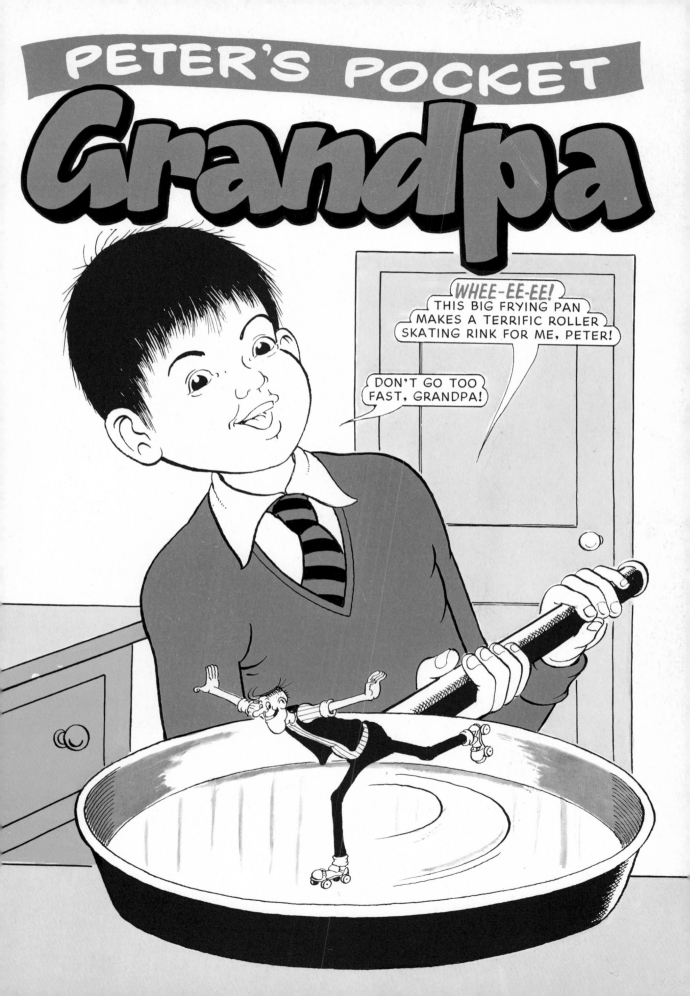

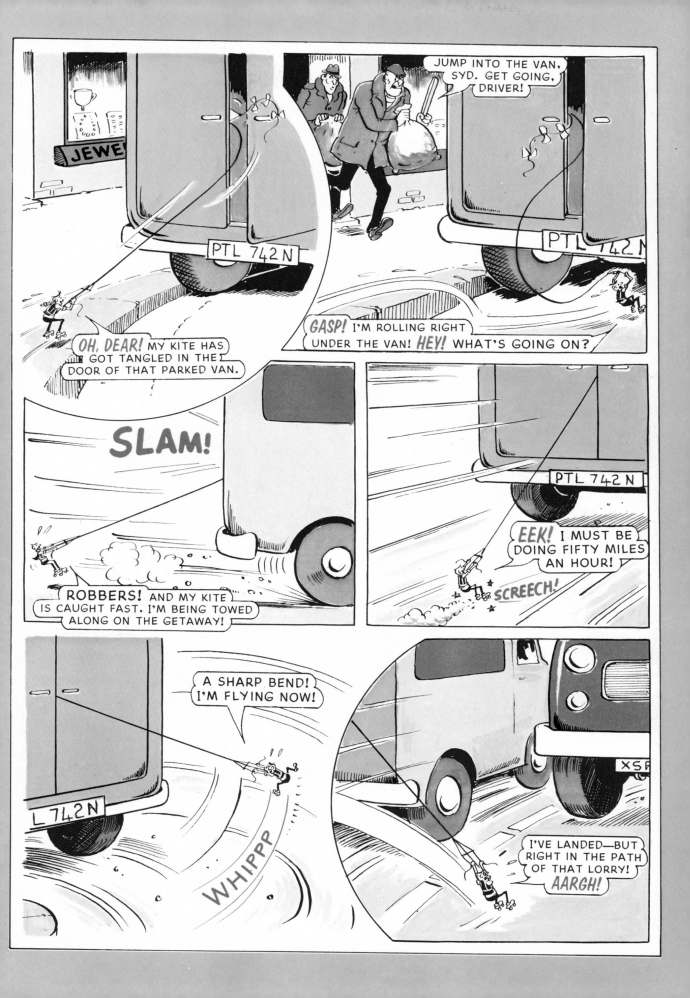

# IZZY SKINT

## HE ALWAYS IS!

HERE'S TWENTY PENCE FOR HELPING ME, IZZY.

THANK YOU.

IT'S NICE OF YOU TO CARRY MY SHOPPING BAG FOR ME, IZZY.

IT'S A PLEASURE, MRS BINKS.

OH, BOY! I WAS SKINT, BUT NOW I'VE GOT TWENTY PENCE. THAT'S NOT TO BE SNEEZED AT!

YOU DID HAVE TWENTY PENCE, IZZY!

BUT NOT NOW!

SNATCH!

YOU'RE RIGHT, TWENTY PENCE ISN'T TO BE SNEEZED AT! HEE-HEE!

BAH! THE ROTTERS!

GOSH! MRS JONES HAS DROPPED SOMETHING FROM HER SHOPPING BASKET!

BUS STOP

MRS JONES! TOO LATE—SHE'S GONE!

BUS STOP

I KNOW WHERE MRS JONES LIVES. SHE'S BOUND TO REWARD ME FOR RETURNING THIS.

PARK

## PUZZLE ANSWERS

### A SUPER " ICE " SCREAM!    SEE PAGES 34—35

1—Slicer, 2—Mice, 3—Notice, 4—Liquorice, 5—Office, 6—Spice, 7—Crevice, 8—Juice, 9—Dice, 10—Policeman, 11—Biceps, 12—Vice, 13—Choice, 14—Venice, 15—Officers, 16—Rice, 17—Voice, 18—Plaice, 19—Advice, 20—Price, 21—Practice, 22—Apprentice, 23—Iceberg.

### SPOT THE " OWL "!    SEE PAGES 98—99

1—Prowler, 2—Blowlamp, 3—Windowledge, 4—Barrowload, 5—Slowly, 6—Bowler, 7—Lowlands, 8—Scowl, 9—Towline, 10—Bowl, 11—Yowl, 12—Bowlegged, 13—Howl, 14—Fowl, 15—Bowler, 16—Bowls, 17—Narrowly, 18—Howler, 19—Knowledge, 20—Growl.